WHEN IN ROME

How many unusual things can you find here?

Illustrated by Terry Kovalcik

KITE CONTEST

Can you find all the pairs of matching kites?

nswer on page 47.

Illustrated by Paul Richer

TWISTERS

Each pair of words here is made up of the same letters. For example, POST and STOP are two different words with the same letters. Use the clues to help you, and you won't go PALE as you LEAP for the answers.

When you've completed each pair, unscramble the letters in yellow to find a related phrase at the bottom.

1. Number before eleven: ___ ___ ___

   It hangs from a basketball hoop: ___ ___ ___

2. Keyboard instrument: ___ ___ ___ ___ ___

   Moan in pain: ___ ___ ___ ___ ___

3. Choice: ___ ___ ___ ___ ___ ___

   Magical liquid or medicine: ___ ___ ___ ___ ___ ___

4. Serpent: ___ ___ ___ ___ ___

   Be tricky or untruthful: ___ ___ ___ ___ ___

5. Pour this on spaghetti: ___ ___ ___ ___ ___

   To make something happen: ___ ___ ___ ___ ___ ___

6. Give out cards in a game: ___ ___ ___ ___

   Take charge, show the way: ___ ___ ___ ___

7. Happening right now in front of you: ___ ___ ___ ___

   Really nasty or morally bad: ___ ___ ___ ___

8. Sound of approaching thunder: ___ ___ ___ ___ ___ ___

   Wood for building: ___ ___ ___ ___ ___ ___

9. Totally quiet: ___ ___ ___ ___ ___ ___

   Try to hear a sound: ___ ___ ___ ___ ___ ___

10. Stone or pebble: ___ ___ ___ ___

    Surface material for a message board: ___ ___ ___ ___

Unscrambled phrase: ___ ___ ___ ___ ___   ___ ___ ___ ___

Answer on page 47.

Illustrated by Gregg Valley

DOT MAGIC

The key to this puzzle is starting at one and joining all the dots
until you reach the grand finale.

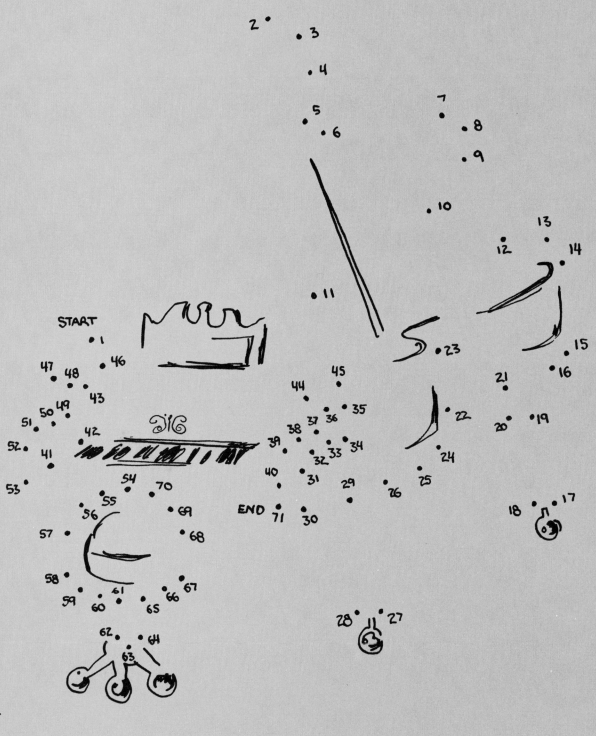

Illustrated by Rob Jones

TOY TIME

Take some time to play around and find the answer to this riddle.
Use the clues to find each letter hidden in this playroom
and then write it in the space above the matching number.

Why did the boy take some spinning toys to school?

```
___ ___   ___ ___ ___ ___ ___ ___   ___ ___   ___ ___   ___ ___ ___ ___
 1   2     3   4   5   6   2   7     6   8     9   2     6   8   10  11
```

```
___ ___   ___ ___ ___   ___ ___ ___ ___ ___ .
12   5     1   12  11    13  14   4   11  11
```

Letter one is on the doll's dress.
Letter three is on the top block.
The front of the truck has letter seven.
One ball has letter fourteen.
Look for letter twelve on the baseball bat.
Letter six is lying among the jacks.
Letter number two is on the racing car.
Letter eleven is caught in the slinky spring.
The fourth letter is on the back of the cowboy's shirt.
Find letter five on the game box.
Letter eight is on the teddy bear's foot.
The dice are all around letter thirteen.
Letter ten is in the elephant's trunk.
The clown has letter nine.

Answer on page 47.

Illustrated by Susanne DeMarco

JIGSAW

Can you tell which pieces below belong in the empty spaces?

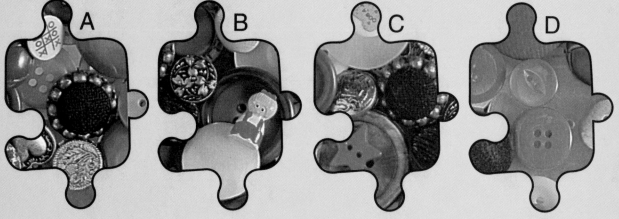

Photo by Jerard Solinger

Answer on page 47.

FREEZEWAYS

Help Sally rejoin her mom.

Illustrated by Charles Jordan

Answer on page 47.

HIDDEN PICTURES

There are at least 21 objects hidden
in this picture. How many can you find?

Illustrated by Maurie Jo Manning

AFRICAN AMERICANS

The names of 42 famous African Americans will fit into these boxes
in one particular way. Write the uppercase names in the correct boxes,
one letter per box. The names in lowercase letters are not included
in the puzzle. Use the number of letters in each word as a clue
to where it will go. Another hint is to look for words
that have similar letters. When you're done,
turn to page 48 to find out why each person is famous.

AARON, Hank
AILEY, Alvin
ALI, Muhammad
ANGELOU, Maya
ASHE, Arthur
ATTUCKS, Crispus
BARAKA, Imamu
BELAFONTE, Harry
BLAKE, Eubie
BLUFORD, Guion S.
BROOKS, Gwendolyn
BROWN, Ron
CARVER, George Washington
CHARLES, Ray

DOUGLASS, Frederick
DU BOIS, W.E.B.
ELLINGTON, Duke
EVERS, Medgar
FITZGERALD, Ella
HALEY, Alex
HUGHES, Langston
JACKSON, Jesse
JOYNER-KERSEE, Jackie
KING, Martin Luther Jr.
MARSHALL, Thurgood
NINO, Pedro Alonzo
OWENS, Jesse
PARKS, Rosa

PATTERSON, Frederick
POITIER, Sidney
POWELL, Colin
REED, Willis
REVELS, Hiram R.
SALEM, Peter
SOJOURNER Truth
STAUPERS, Mabel K.
SUTTON, Percy
TUBMAN, Harriet
TURNER, Nat
WALKER, Alice
WILSON, August
YOUNG, Andrew

Answer on page 47.

TRI SUM

Fill in each circle in this figure with one of the numbers from 1 to 19. The trick is that the sum of any three circles that make up the side of a triangle should total 22. No number will appear more than once. We've put in a few numbers to start you off.

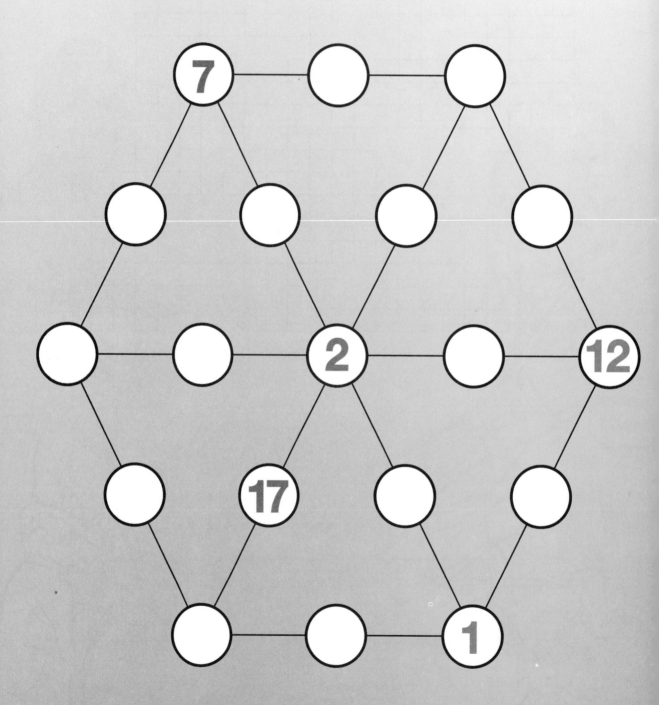

Answer on page 48.

INSTANT PICTURE

Hey, don't dawdle as you fiddle with this.
Just fill in all the areas containing two dots to get a jump on it.

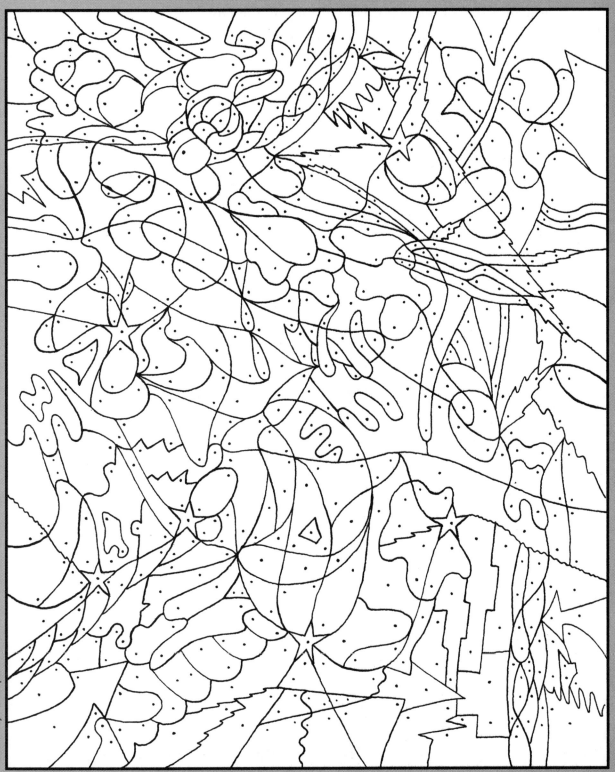

Illustrated by Rob Sepanak

GLOBE PROBE

That intrepid explorer, Dr. Cincinnati Holmes, is quite content.
He's thinking about drifting over the continents. You can help by
identifying the areas that make up the seven continents of the world.

A continent is one of the major land masses on the globe. The
name of each continent is listed below. It's up to you to draw a line
from the name to where the continents are located on the map.

North America

South America

Europe

Asia

Africa

Oceania (Australia)

Antarctica

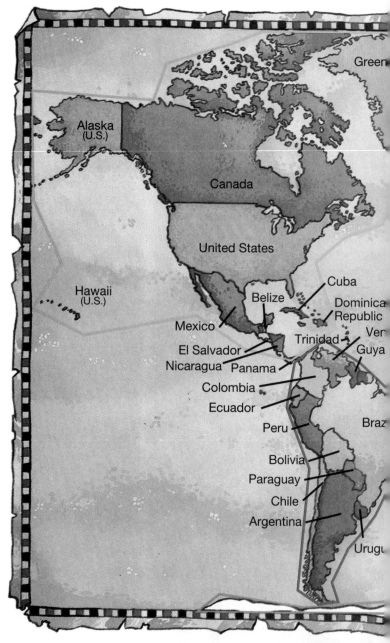

Illustrated by John Nez

PARTY TIME

How many differences can you see between these two pictures?

Illustrated by Stephen Sweney

EVERYTHING IS ALL "IGHT"

Use the clues to find each word below.

1. Number that fits in this category : ___ IGHT

2. Your eyes provide this sense: ___ IGHT

3. Not heavy: ___ IGHT

4. Not loose: ___ IGHT

5. Absolutely correct: ___ IGHT

6. Argue with someone: ___ IGHT

7. How tall something is:
___ ___ IGHT

8. How heavy something is:
___ ___ IGHT

9. Flimsy or thin: ___ ___ IGHT

10. Serves a king: ___ ___ IGHT

11. Extremely smart:
___ ___ IGHT

12. To scare or surprise:
___ ___ IGHT ___ ___

13. 12 o'clock p.m.:
___ ___ ___ ___ IGHT

14. Not crooked:
___ ___ ___ ___ IGHT

Illustrated by Tom Powers

Answer on page 48.

CAT & DOG MYSTERY

Case # 222
The Haunted Library

"Be careful," Jason Jackal warned as he carefully pushed open the doors to his new home. "The ghosts may still be here."

Jason had burst into the police station ten minutes ago, screaming that ghosts had haunted him right out of Usher House, a big, fancy mansion on the outskirts of town. Jason had purchased Usher House last year. He had wanted to tear down the old mansion to build a shopping mall. But the town council had declared Usher House to be a historical landmark. Since he couldn't do anything else with it, Jason finally moved into the place just last week.

The detectives rushed over to Usher House.

Weird noises could be heard coming from the old place. It sounded like the house was moaning. The noise went on for a few moments before finally stopping.

Now the three were gathered together on the porch, about to enter the dark and creepy house.

Inside, the house was pitch black, except for the light given off by three tall candles set in individual holders on a nearby table. The flames flickered as the threesome entered, the draft creating dancing images on the highly polished candlesticks.

Deductive Dog grabbed one candlestick off the spotless table, handing another to his partner, Cat.

"Be careful," he warned. "Watch those flames in this old house."

"And watch out for those spirits," said Jason.

The trio began searching the house for ghosts.

"It all started in here," Jason said.

He led them through some double doors into a library. Books of all sorts normally filled these dusty shelves, but now the room was a wreck. Papers were everywhere, books had been tossed all about, and even a small set of shelves had been pushed over.

"I don't see any ghosts," Dog whispered.

"They're here all right," said Jason. The candlelight etched his face with deep shadows. "I feel them all around us."

"Why don't you tell us what happened," said Dog.

"I was in the library, working late. I keep the lights off to save on electricity, so I use candles. I find it kind of romantic. All those old books, the soft glow of candlelight, the quiet solitude . . ."

"If we can focus on these ghosts," Dog grumbled.

"Oh, sorry. I had lit these candles and put them on my table. After about an hour, I began to hear a strange moaning sound. When I went to investigate, books flew off the shelf at me. A strong wind whirled into the room. It picked me up and tossed me into the hall. That's when I ran out of the house."

"Whatever was here seems to be gone now," Dog said.

"The council will have to let me tear this place down now," said Jason. "They won't want to have a real haunted house around. There's no telling what might happen with these ghosts on the loose."

"I'm not worried," Cat whispered to Dog. "It shouldn't be too hard to shed some light on this ghost story."

WHAT CLUE DOES CAT HAVE?

Once you solve this case, find all the ghosts that are haunting the library.

COLD COMFORT

Can you tell which sister is wearing which scarf?

Answer on page 48.

Illustrated by T.F. Cook

ON SITE

To be a pro player, you'll need to unscramble each sport site below. Each place is where you can go to watch or play the game listed above it. When you've unscrambled them all, read the letters in orange to find a mystery word.

Hockey	Basketball	Rugby	Bowling	Football	Racing	Baseball	Golf	Soccer
NEARA	TROCU	CHIPT	YALEL	LIFED	KARTC	MANODDI	USCORE	MUSTADI
1	2	3	4	5	6	7	8	9

Illustrated by Anthony Accardo

1. ___ ___ ___ ___ ___   4. ___ ___ ___ ___ ___   7. ___ ___ ___ ___ ___ ___ ___

2. ___ ___ ___ ___ ___   5. ___ ___ ___ ___ ___   8. ___ ___ ___ ___ ___ ___

3. ___ ___ ___ ___ ___   6. ___ ___ ___ ___ ___   9. ___ ___ ___ ___ ___ ___ ___

Mystery Word: ___ ___ ___ ___ ___ ___ ___ ___ ___

Answer on page 48.

PICTURE MIXER

Copy these mixed-up squares in the spaces on the next page
to put this picture back together. The letters and numbers tell you where
each square belongs. The first one, A-3, has been done for you.

A-3   A-1   A-2   A-4

B-2   B-1   B-4   B-3

C-4   C-3   C-2   C-1

D-4   D-2   D-1   D-3

Illustrated by M. Gugliotta

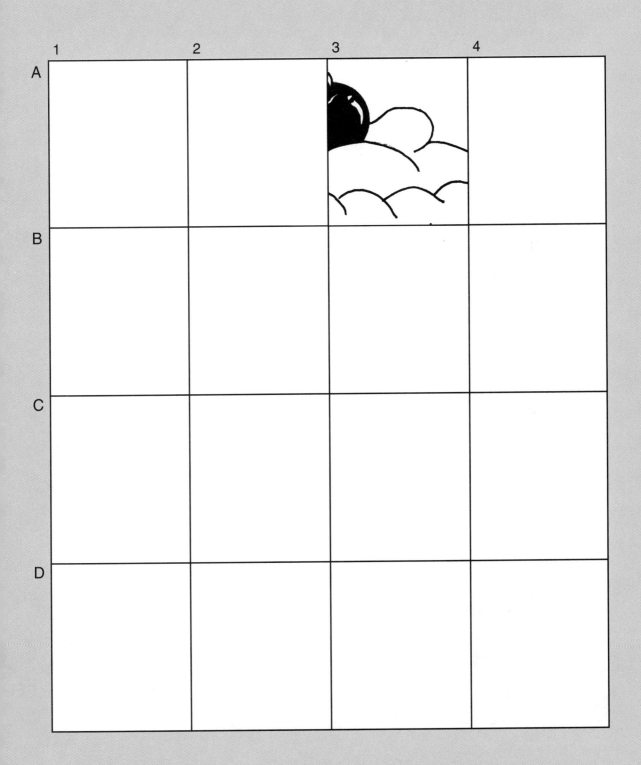

ROW, ROW, ROW

Every booth here has something in common with
the two others in the same row.
For example, there's a hat on each table
in the top three booths across.
Look at the other diners across, down, and diagonally.
Can you tell what's the same in each row of three?

Illustrated by Bill Colrus

Answer on page 49.

MUSEUM MEMORIES   Part I

Take a long look at this picture. Try to remember everything you see in it. Then turn the page, and try to answer some questions about it without looking back.

DON'T READ THIS UNTIL YOU HAVE LOOKED AT "Museum Memories—Part I" ON PAGE 29.

MUSEUM MEMORIES   Part II

Can you answer these questions about the museum scene you saw? Don't peek!

1. What dinosaurs are featured in this exhibit?

2. How many animals are wearing glasses?

3. How many pigs are wearing hats?

4. Are there mice in this museum?

5. Is anyone sleeping?

6. How many exit signs can be seen?

7. What is the lion eating?

8. Who is crying?

9. Where is the baby giraffe hiding?

Answer on page 49.

TETRAN

Can you fit all these pieces into the yellow square below?
All pieces must be used and none may overlap. You may want to copy
the pieces onto another page before working the puzzle.

Answer on page 49.

HERE TO THERE

Read the road signs to figure the following distances by adding or subtracting. All posted distances are in miles from your current location. Write the answer in the first space after each question. Then look at the mileage chart at the bottom. Write the letter that matches the mileage in the space beside the mileage you've written. When you're done, read down the column of letters to find the answer to the riddle.

What's the best way to talk to someone who is eating onions?

How far is it from:

	Mileage	Letter
1. Blue Water to Green Bay?	___	___
2. Deer Park to Crystal River?	___	___
3. Red Mountain to Green Bay?	___	___
4. Blue Water to Red Mountain?	___	___
5. Long Lake to Fish Lake?	___	___
6. Deer Park to Long Lake?	___	___
7. Crystal River to Green Bay?	___	___
8. Clear Lake to Crystal River?	___	___
9. Foggy Bottom to Green Bay?	___	___
10. Fish Lake to Clear Lake?	___	___
11. Long Lake to Crystal River?	___	___
12. Blue Water to Foggy Bottom?	___	___

Mileage Chart

5	20	25	55	60	85
I	D	T	C	O	S

100	120	140	240	360
N	A	G	L	E

Road signs:
- DEER PARK 15 MI.
- BLUE WATER 200 MI.
- FISH LAKE 30 MI.
- CLEAR LAKE 70 MI.
- GREEN BAY 40 MI.
- RED MOUNTAIN 60 MI.
- LONG LAKE 10 MI.
- CRYSTAL RIVER 45 MI.
- FOGGY BOTTOM 160 MI.

Illustrated by Marc Nadel

Answer on page 49.

BONE DIG

This archaeologist has just been buried in work today.
You can help by digging up the names of
27 different bones that are hidden in these letters.
Look up, down, backward, across, or diagonally.

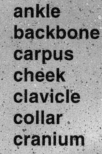

ankle
backbone
carpus
cheek
clavicle
collar
cranium

femur
fibula
heel
hip
jaw
mastoid
pelvis

radius
rib
shin
shoulder
skull
spine

sternum
tarsus
thigh
tibia
ulna

vertebra
wrist

Illustrated by Jerry Zimmerman

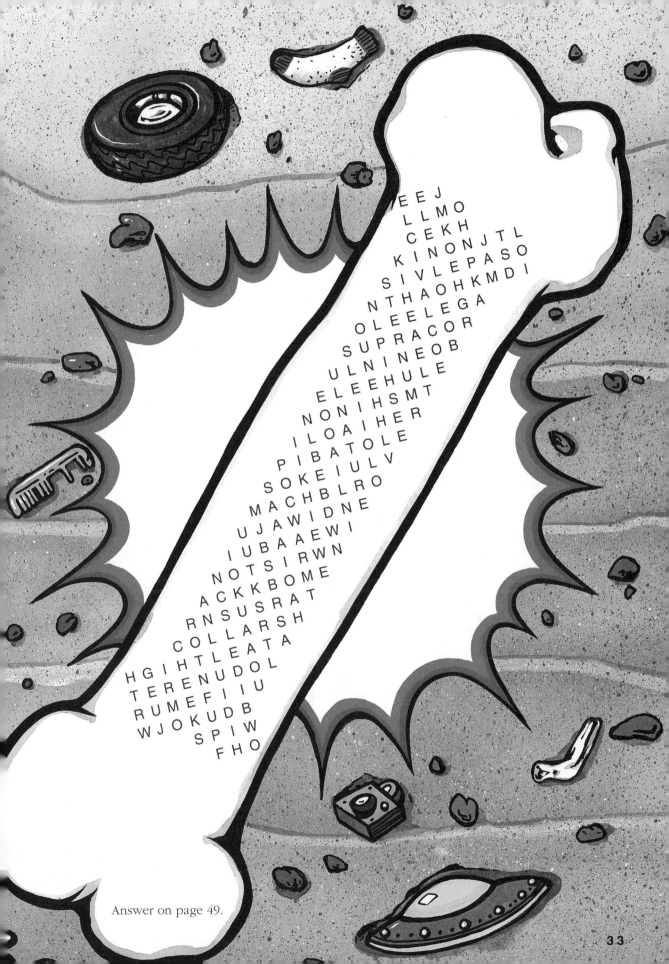

Answer on page 49.

STUFFED SHIRT

Can you number the pictures to show what happened
first, second, and so on?

Illustrated by Sherry Neidigh

Answer on page 49.

STOP, LOOK, AND LIST

Under each category, list three things that
begin with the letter S.

WINTER SPORTS

S _____

S _____

S _____

WINTER CLOTHES

S _____

S _____

S _____

WINTER VEHICLES

S _____

S _____

S _____

WINTER WEATHER

S _____

S _____

S _____

Illustrated by Lisa Dayer

Answer on page 49.

THE SPIES OF LIFE

This code is so secret even we don't know what it means. These undercover operators are sending riddles to one another. Can you take the first letter of each object pictured to decipher the messages?

WHAT'S NEXT?

Look at the blocks in each row across.
Can you guess which of the two boxes belongs in the blank?

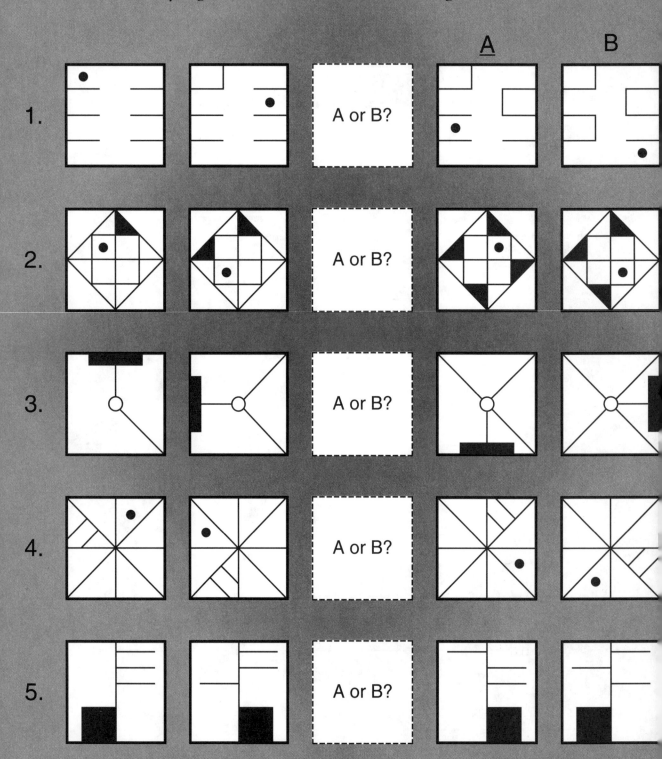

Answer on page 50.

BITS AND BYTES

This blank screen does not compute.
Use your imagination to draw in what you like to see on a computer.
Is it a dinosaur from an encyclopedia or a spaceship from a game?
It's up to you to key in the right image.

SHOE THING

The Lewis family has five children, three boys (Ed, Fred, and Ted) and two girls (Lara and Clara). Each is a good kid, but none of them can ever remember to put his or her athletic shoes back in the closet. Yesterday, their mother found one of each child's shoes in ten different places! To sort this out, use the information in the clues to match each shoe with its owner and to say where each shoe was found. Here's a hint: though two shoes were found in each place, they were not always from the same pair.

Two athletic shoes were in the kitchen — one was under the sink, the other was in the refrigerator.

Two were in the living room — one on top of the television, the other under the couch.

Two were in the bathroom — one in the bathtub, the other in the wastebasket.

Two were in the boys' bedroom — one was in a dresser drawer, the other was hanging from a lamp.

Two were outside — one was under the porch, the other was in the doghouse.

1. The five pairs of shoes are: the pair of Yikey's, the shoe found in the kitchen sink and its mate (which was not outside), the pair found under the couch and hanging from the lamp, the pair belonging to Ed, and the Queds (which don't belong to Clara).

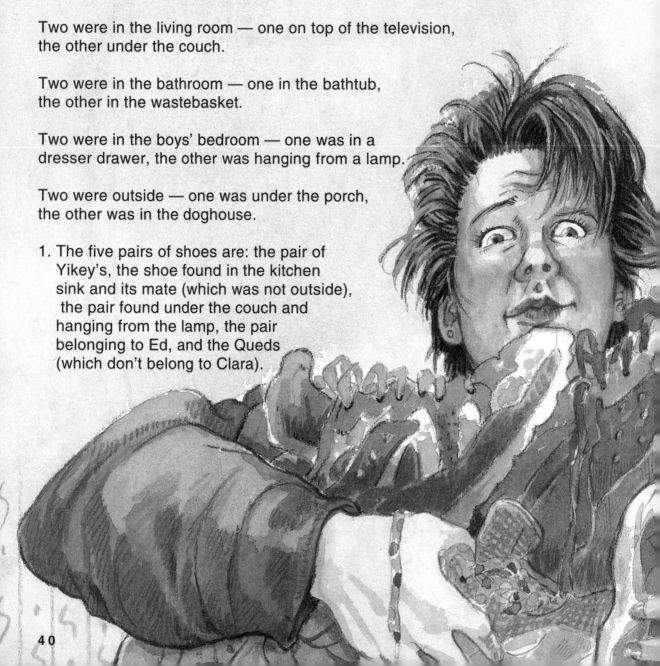

2. One of the Yikey's was in the living room; the other one was outside. Neither the Queds nor the Woyts were in the kitchen.

3. One of Ted's shoes (which are not the ZZgear) was in the same room as one of Ed's; Ted's other shoe was in his dresser drawer.

4. Both of Fred's shoes were in the same room. Neither Clara's shoes nor the mate to the shoe found in the refrigerator was in the doghouse.

	\multicolumn{5}{c}{1st location}	\multicolumn{5}{c}{2nd location}	\multicolumn{5}{c}{owner}
	sink	TV	tub	couch	fridge	drawer	doghouse	wastebasket	lamp	porch	Ed	Fred	Clara	Lara	Ted
Bebops															
Yikey's															
Queds															
Woyts															
ZZGear															
Ed															
Fred															
Clara															
Lara															
Ted															
drawer															
d. house															
w. basket															
lamp															
porch															

Answer on page 50.

Illustrated by Anni Matsick

CLOSE CALLS

Can you tell what common household tool
is featured in each close-up photo?

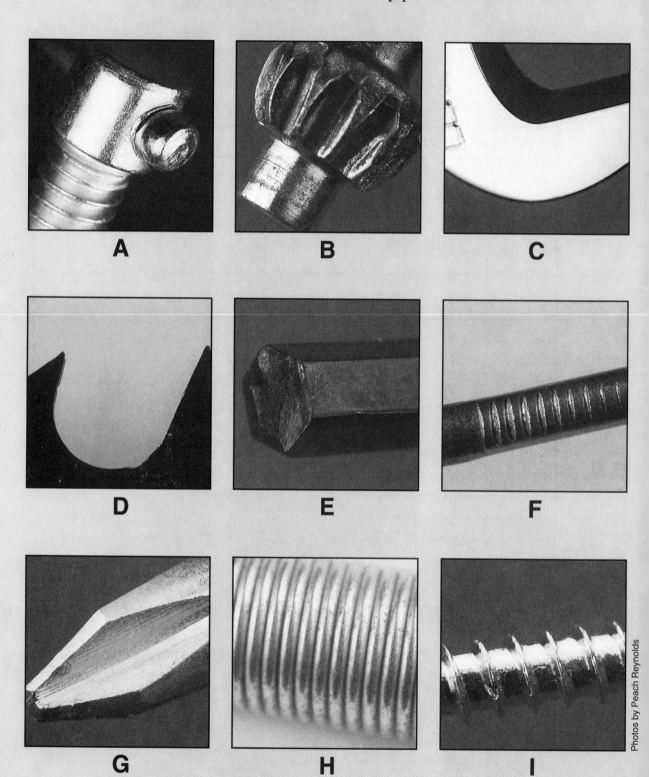

A

B

C

D

E

F

G

H

I

Photos by Peach Reynolds

Answer on page 50.

WHAT'S IN A WORD?

The problem with building sandcastles is the sand sometimes shifts and is hard to control. You won't have a grain of trouble if you can control this puzzle by shifting the letters in SANDCASTLE. Come up with as many words as you can that are at least three-letters long. None of them can be plurals that end in "s." Can you build at least 65 words?

Illustrated by Chuck Dillon

Answer on page 50.

PEOPLE PLUS

Look for different people in the clues. When you come up
with a word that matches the clue given, write it in the
boxes, one letter per box. Some clues may be a bit difficult,
so work back and forth to find all the words that fit.

ACROSS

1. Someone who goes into space
9. Someone who performs in a play
10. Small character from fantasy, seen in gardens
12. Red-colored horses
13. Spanish for Matthew, city in California: San _____
14. Color or dye
15. Puts in the mail a second time
17. Asian area made up of Vietnam, Cambodia, Laos, and others: _____china
18. Suffix for a person who belongs to a certain area, like from Brooklyn and Israel
19. a, b, _, _, _, f
20. Turn rapidly in place
23. Someone who works with students
27. Table tennis, _____ Pong
28. Mistake
29. To make very happy
30. Singers between sopranos and tenors
31. Someone who eats at a restaurant
32. Someone who watches a sporting event or concert

DOWN

1. What you put into a parking meter or pay phone (2 words)
2. To get out of a chair or bed
3. The Lone Ranger's partner
4. Abbreviation for railroads
5. Wide open, like a person's mouth
6. Old English meaning to give something to someone, "I bestow _____ you..."
7. Five of these are on each foot
8. Myself
9. Someone who paints or sculpts
11. Witty word or remark
13. The machine someone checks to see if you've been parked too long
15. Someone who sits on a horse or motorcycle
16. One who produces musical notes from the throat
19. Selected something
20. Break in half with force or divide evenly
21. Keyboard instrument
22. Between two like things or areas
24. Long, wiggly fish
25. Works that include music, painting, sculpting, writing, etc.
26. What you plant and harvest
29. Abbreviation for Estimated Date of Arrival
30. Abbreviation for early time of day

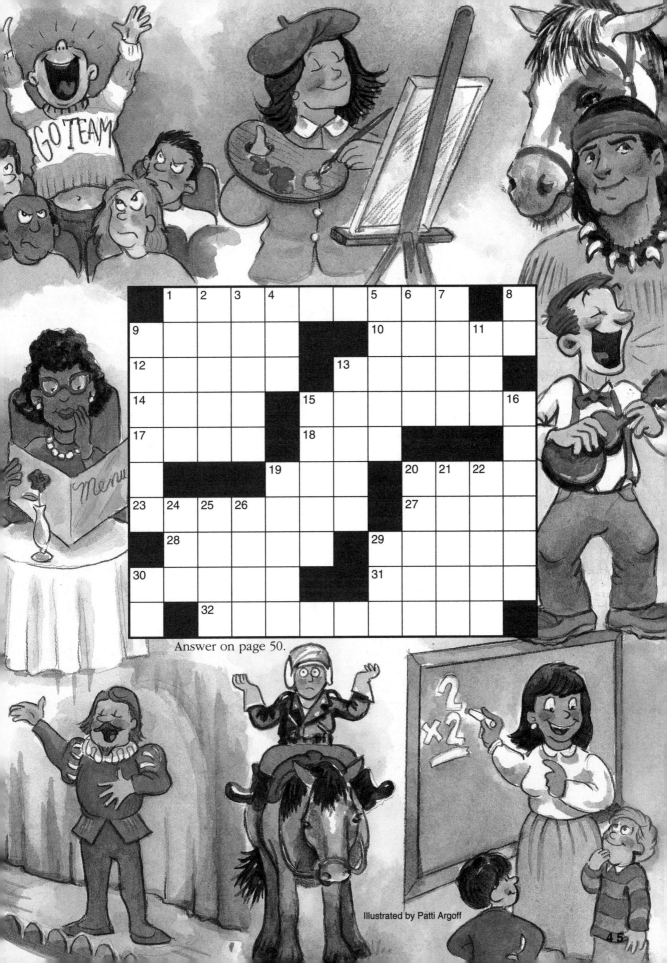

Answer on page 50.

Illustrated by Patti Argoff

45

SERPENTINE SHELLS

Several serpents are silently slithering in this scene.
See how many snakes you can spot.

Illustrated by Judith Hunt

ANSWERS

COVER

4 5
3 6
2 1

KITE CONTEST (pages 4-5)

TWISTERS (page 6)

1. ten
   net
2. organ
   groan
3. option
   potion
4. snake
   sneak
5. sauce
   cause
6. deal
   lead
7. live
   evil
8. rumble
   lumber
9. silent
   listen
10. rock
    cork

Unscrambled letters:
Double take

DOT MAGIC (page 7)

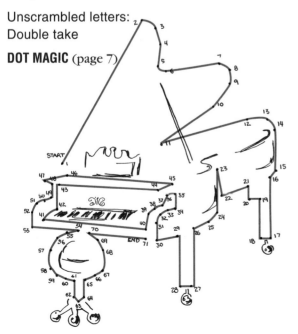

TOY TIME (pages 8-9)

Why did the boy take some spinning toys to school? He wanted to be tops in his class.

JIGSAW (page 10)

1-C, 2-D, 3-A, B is left over

FREEZEWAYS (page 11)

AFRICAN AMERICANS (pages 14-15)

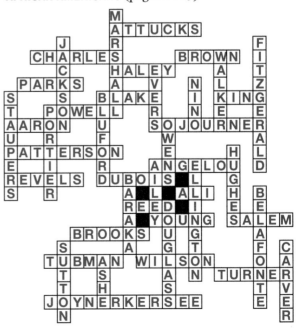

AFRICAN AMERICANS (pages 14-15)

AARON - Baseball player
AILEY - Dancer
ALI - Boxer
ANGELOU - Poet
ASHE - Tennis player
ATTUCKS - Patriot
BARAKA - Playwright
BELAFONTE - Singer
BLAKE - Musician
BLUFORD - Astronaut
BROOKS - Poet
BROWN - Diplomat
CARVER - Scientist
CHARLES - Entertainer
DOUGLASS - Abolitionist
DU BOIS - Cofounder NAACP
ELLINGTON - Musician
EVERS - Civil rights leader
FITZGERALD - Singer
HALEY - Author
HUGHES - Poet
JACKSON - Religious leader
JOYNER-KERSEE - Athlete
KING - Civil rights leader
MARSHALL - U.S. Supreme Court judge
NINO - Navigator
OWENS - Athlete
PARKS - Civil rights leader
PATTERSON - Educator
POITIER - Actor
POWELL - General
REED - Basketball player
REVELS - Clergyman
SALEM - Patriot
SOJOURNER Truth - Abolitionist
STAUPERS - Nurse
SUTTON - Politician
TUBMAN - Abolitionist
TURNER - Slave revolt leader
WALKER - Author
WILSON - Playwright
YOUNG - Diplomat

TRI SUM (page 16)

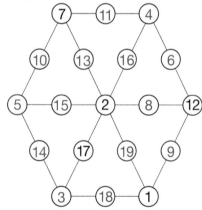

INSTANT PICTURE (page 17)

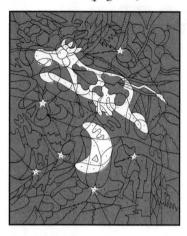

EVERYTHING IS ALL "IGHT" (page 21)

1. eight
2. sight
3. light
4. tight
5. right
6. fight
7. height
8. weight
9. slight
10. knight
11. bright
12. frighten
13. midnight
14. straight

CAT & DOG (pages 22-23)

CASE #222 - THE HAUNTED LIBRARY

Jason Jackal claimed that the candles were burning for longer than an hour. Yet when the group came into the house, the candles were still tall in their holders, and there was no wax either on the candlestick or on the table. When confronted by the detectives, Jackal admitted that his story was all part of a scheme to get the town to allow him to tear the Usher House down.

COLD COMFORT (page 24)

1-C, 2-B, 3-D, 4-A

ON SITE (page 25)

1. Arena
2. Court
3. Pitch
4. Alley
5. Field
6. Track
7. Diamond
8. Course
9. Stadium

Mystery Word: ATHLETICS

GLOBE PROBE (pages 18-19)

North America
South America
Europe
Asia
Africa
Oceania (Australia)
Antarctica

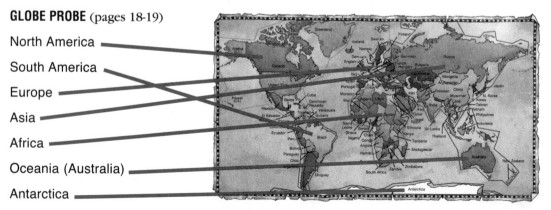

PICTURE MIXER (pages 26-27)

ROW, ROW, ROW (page 28)

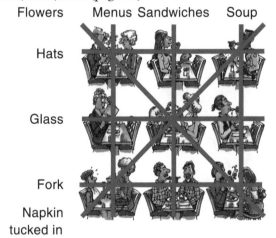

Flowers Menus Sandwiches Soup

Hats

Glass

Fork

Napkin
tucked in

MUSEUM MEMORIES (page 30)

1. Stegosaurus and
   Tyrannosaurus Rex
2. Three
3. Two
4. Yes
5. Yes
6. Two
7. Frankfurter or hot dog
8. The mother giraffe
9. Behind the palm tree

TETRAN (page 30)

Here is our answer. You may have found another.

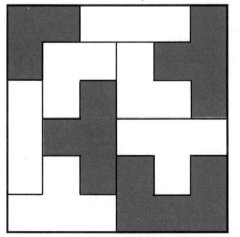

HERE TO THERE (page 31)

1. 240 miles   L
2. 60 miles   O
3. 100 miles   N
4. 140 miles   G
5. 20 miles   D
6. 5 miles   I
7. 85 miles   S
8. 25 miles   T
9. 120 miles   A
10. 100 miles   N
11. 55 miles   C
12. 360 miles   E

What's the best way to talk to someone who is eating onions? Long distance

BONE DIG (pages 32-33)

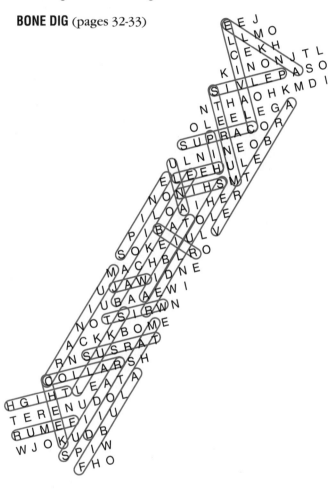

STUFFED SHIRT (page 34)

2   5
4   1
3   6

STOP, LOOK, AND LIST (page 35)

WINTER SPORTS

Skiing   Skating   Sledding

WINTER CLOTHES

Scarf   Socks   Snowsuit

WINTER VEHICLES

Sleigh   Snowmobile   Snowplow

WINTER WEATHER

Sleet   Snow   Sunshine

THE SPIES OF LIFE (pages 36-37)
Why do undercover agents always tell jokes?
  Because they're wise guy spies.
I despise the spy's disguise.
  Say that three times fast!

WHAT'S NEXT? (page 38)
1. A   4. B
2. B   5. B
3. A

SHOE THING (pages 40-41)
Ed does not own the Yikey's or the Queds (clue 1). One of the Yikey's (living room and outside - clue 2) is not the one found under the couch (clue 1); it was on top of the television. The Queds were not in the sink or under the couch (clue 1); nor were they in the fridge (clue 2); one of the Queds was in the bathtub. Both of Fred's shoes were in the same room (clue 4); so, his shoes were in the bathroom; one in the bathtub, and the other in the wastebasket. Fred owns the Queds. The Woyts were not in the sink or the fridge (clue 2); therefore they were under the couch. The mate of the shoe found under the couch was hanging from the lamp (clue 1). This pair of shoes did not belong to Ed (clue 1), Fred (clue 4) or Ted (clue 3), they belong to either Lara or Clara. One of Ed's shoes was not in the sink or under the couch (clue 1); nor on the TV nor in the tub (above); Ed's shoe was in the refrigerator. One of Ted's shoes was in the dresser drawer (clue 3); his other shoe was not under the couch (clue 1). Therefore, since Ed's other shoe was not hanging from the lamp, Ted's other shoe was in the kitchen sink (clue 3). By elimination, Lara's shoes were the one in the doghouse and the one on the TV. Clara owns the Woyts. Ted does not own the ZZgear (clue 3); therefore, he owns the Bebops. Ed owns the ZZgears.
In summary:
Bebops - sink & dresser drawer - Ted
Yikey's - TV & doghouse - Lara
Queds - tub & wastebasket - Fred
Woyts - couch & lamp - Clara
ZZgear - refrigerator & porch - Ed

CLOSE CALLS (page 42)
A. clamp   F. nail
B. chuck key   G. screwdriver
C. crescent wrench H. spring
D. saw   I. screw
E. hex key

WHAT'S IN A WORD? (page 43)
We found 78 words.
You may have found others.

ace	castle	east	led	seal
act	cat	eat	lend	seat
alas	cent	enact	lens	send
and	clad	end	lent	sent
ant	clan	lace	less	slate
ascend	class	lad	neat	stale
ascent	clean	laden	nest	stance
assent	cleat	lance	net	stand
asset	dale	land	sad	steal
cad	dance	lane	salad	tale
can	data	lass	sale	tan
canal	date	last	salt	tea
cane	deal	late	sand	ten
candle	dean	lead	scale	tend
case	den	lean	scent	
cast	dent	least	sea	

PEOPLE PLUS (pages 44-45)

A	S	T	R	O	N	A	U	T		M
A	C	T	O	R		G	N	O	M	E
R	O	A	N	S		M	A	T	E	O
T	I	N	T		R	E	P	O	S	T	S
I	N	D	O		I	T	E			I
S				C	D	E		S	P	I	N
T	E	A	C	H	E	R		P	I	N	G
	E	R	R	O	R		E	L	A	T	E
A	L	T	O	S			D	I	N	E	R
M		S	P	E	C	T	A	T	O	R

Art Director: Timothy J. Gillner • Designer: Glenn Boyd
Project Director: Jeffrey A. O'Hare • Editorial Consultant: Andrew Gutelle • Design Consultant: Bob Feldgus
Copy Editor: Juanita Galuska • Production Coordinator: Sarah Robinson

Puzzle Contributors
Celia Baron • Madeline Cohen • Beth Gehred-O'Connell • Jeanette C. Grote
Rich Latta • Clare Mishica • Donna Lugg Pape • Sherry Timberman